A book of birthday thoughts for you
In honor of your day,
With warmest wishes for a year
That's happy in every way!

All About Birthdays

*Thoughts on
Growing Up
by the Peanuts
Characters*

Illustrated by Charles M. Schulz

When you
stop adding
"and a half"
to your age.

*When you suddenly realize
that to some people,
"the older generation"
is you.*

When you can remember when "long hair" music meant "classical."

*When you
still have a cake,
but not a candle
for every
year.*

*When you learn
to do without things
for a while.*

*When
you no longer
want to stay up
"just ten minutes more."*

When you pick out a cereal
that tastes good,
even if it doesn't have a
"secret agent decoder ring"
with a hidden compartment.

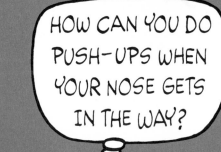

*You know you're
growing up
when it gets
harder and harder
to stay in shape.*

When peanut butter gets harder to digest.

*When
the crowd
is always
one dance
ahead
of you.*

*When
your
naturally curly
hair
doesn't stay
curly
so naturally.*

When
you think twice
about your
daring exploits.

*You can tell
you're growing up
when you confront
problems maturely.*

When
you realize
that all
your
dreams of glory
won't come true.

*When
you start
taking baths
because
you want to.*

*When
thoughts of school
are happy thoughts.*

*When
you have mastered
the art
of self-control.*

z

z

z

z

When
you start wishing
you had
an afternoon nap
again.

TO YOU....
BIRTHDAY TO YOU.

ou're growing up.

Editorial Direction: Arnold Shapiro and Arthur Wortman
Design: David Jenkins and William Peterson